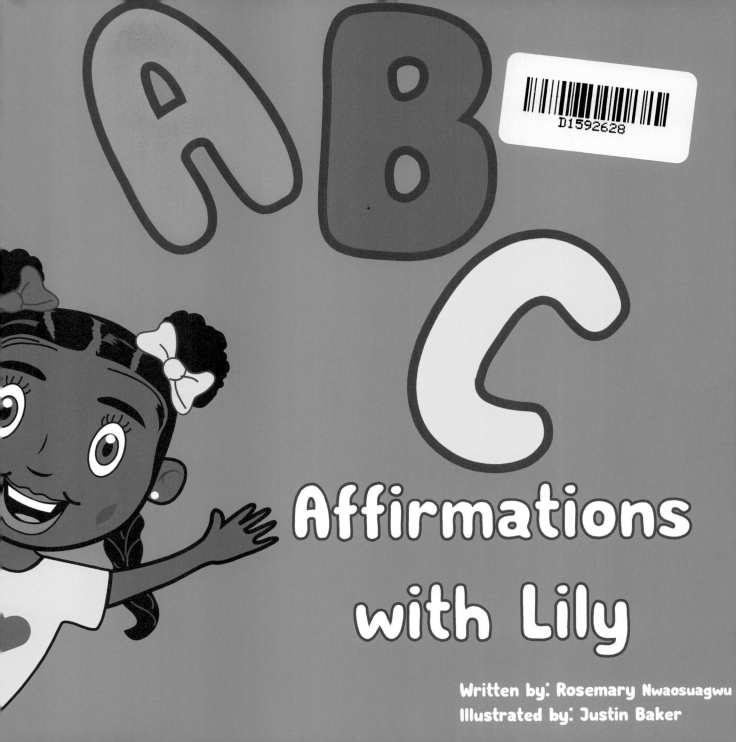

ABC

Affirmations with Lily

Written by: Rosemary Nwaosuagwu

Illustrated by: Justin Baker

D1592628

This book is from:

_____

To you:

_____

ABC Affirmations with LILY

ISBN: 978-0-578-82279-2

Illustration and artwork created digitally by:
Justin Baker
Printed in the USA

DEDICATION

To my Mommy, who always motivates me
to be the best that I can
be each and every day.
I love you so much.

Hi, I'm Lily.
Do you know that you are unique
in every way? There is no one like you. You
are special each and every day! Come along
and read with me my ABC Affirmations from
A through Z. Remember when you are done,
continue to be the best that you can be!

I am **AMAZING**, yes indeed.
From my head down to my toes,
all I have to do is believe.

I am **BRAVE**. I am always standing tall.
Believing in myself, is the best of all.

I am **CONFIDENT** in everything that I do,
I know that I can achieve
anything that I set my mind to.

I can **DREAM** big. I know what I want to be; to be a leader, is my destiny!

I always put **EFFORTS** in all that I do, trying my best at all times is important for not just me, but also for you.

I have **FAITH** in myself because I know that I can do anything; I can dance; I can roller-skate; and I can even sing.

I am destined for GREATNESS,
and I know I can lead.
I can be the best because
I believe in ME!

I am **HELPFUL** to everyone.
Helping others can
be a lot of fun.

O

I am **IMPORTANT** you should know.
I always hold my head high and never low

J

I am **JOYFUL** everyday, because I know that I am unique in every way.

K

I am **KIND** to others which is the best way to be.
Showing love and kindness is a good deed.

L

I am a **LEADER**, ready to lead.
Creating peace and harmony in this world,
is what we need.

M

I **MOTIVATE** myself each and everyday.
Setting and reaching my goals is my way

I am **NOBLE** because I am
honest which is very true.
Telling the truth at all times
is a good thing that I do.

I am an **ORIGINAL**, there is only one me. Trying my best, doing my best, and knowing **I CAN** is key.

P

I have a **PURPOSE** to follow my dreams,
to reach my goals and to achieve.

I will never give up! I will never QUIT!
I will never say "I can't do it",
even for one bit.

I am **RESPECTFUL** to all those around me:
To my family, to my teachers,
and friends who make me happy.

I am **SPECIAL**. I love everything about me, because I know that I am unique in every single way.

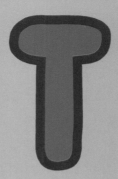

I am TALENTED. Can't you see?
If I set my mind to it,
I can be anything that I want to be.

I am **UNIQUE** in every way.
There is so much in life that I can gain
when I am doing my best, in my own lane

I am **VALUABLE** and have confidence that I can succeed, because I believe in myself and follow my dreams!

I am eXTRAORDINARY-this I know.
Everything I go
through helps me grow.

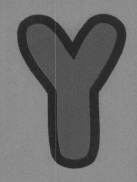

I am **YOUTHFUL** and proud.
I like to speak above the crowd.

Z

I am ZESTFUL because I always follow my dreams. I will continue to believe in myself and know that I too can achieve!

Good Job. I hope you have enjoyed these affirmations from A through Z. Always remember: You can achieve, be, and do anything that you set your mind to. Never give up on your dreams. Believe in yourself, and you can and will achieve.

t's review the affirmations that we have
arned from A through Z:

Amazing   K: Kind   U: Unique
Brave   L: Leader   V: Valuable
Confident   M: Motivate   W: Worthy
Dream   N: Noble   X: eXtraordinary
Efforts   O: Original   Y: Youthful
Faith   P: Purpose   Z: Zestful
Greatness   Q: Quit
Helpful   R: Respectful
Important   S: Special
Joyful   T: Talented

Let's Practice:

Write down three affirmations that you can say each and every day.

1.

_____

2.

_____

3.

_____

To order bulk of this book for your organization, Daycare or school, please send email to: booksbyrossy@gmail.com

CPSIA information can be obtained
at www.ICGtesting.com
Printed in the USA
LVHW070114160121
676628LV00001B/5